A Teddy Horsley Book

The Picnic

Teddy Horsley goes to Communion
Based on Mark 8

by Leslie J Francis and Nicola M Slee
Pictures by Laura Cooper

The Bear facts:
The Teddy Horsley Bible Series is designed to build bridges between the young child's day to day experiences of the world and major biblical themes and stories.

Both authors work in church-related institutions of education. Nicola Slee is Director of Studies at the Aston Training Scheme in Birmingham. Leslie Francis is Professor of Pastoral Theology at the University of Wales, Lampeter, and Trinity College, Carmarthen. The illustrator, Laura Cooper, is a teacher and artist.

The Teddy Horsley Series is a result of extensive research into the religious development of young children, and the authors' and illustrator's wide experience of educational work in schools and churches.

Published by:
National Christian Education Council
1020 Bristol Road
Selly Oak
Birmingham
B29 6LB

British Library Cataloguing in Publication Data:
A catalogue record for this book is available from the British Library.

Text © Leslie J Francis and Nicola M Slee 1996 revised
Illustrations © National Christian Education Council 1996

Unless otherwise stated, quotations from the Bible are from the *Good News Bible*, published by the Bible Societies/Collins, © American Bible Society, New York, 1966, 1971, 1976.

First published 1983 Collins   ISBN 0-7197-0857-5   Printed in England
Revised edition 1996

Teddy Horsley is a bear who likes Sundays.

On Sundays Teddy Horsley goes picnicking with

Mr and Mrs Henry, Lucy and Walter, and Betsy Bear.

They bring crusty bread, yellow cheese,
and a fat jar of raspberry jam.

They bring hard green apples,
sparkling lemonade, and rich red wine.

They munch, they chatter, they laugh:

they celebrate their picnic.

Mrs Henry takes out her camera.
Mr Henry packs away the picnic.

Lucy and Walter fly their kite.
Teddy Horsley and Betsy Bear lick the jam jar clean.

Everyone is happy.

Teddy Horsley is a bear who likes Sundays.

On Sundays Teddy Horsley goes to church with

Mr and Mrs Henry, Lucy and Walter, and Betsy Bear.

They bring bread on a silver plate,
and a pair of candles.

They bring wine, a silver cup,
and water in a glass jar.

They sing, they worship, they share:

they celebrate the communion.

Mr and Mrs Henry lead some prayers together.

Lucy and Walter lead the singing.
Teddy Horsley and Betsy Bear play under the pew.

Mr and Mrs Henry, Lucy and Walter come to the rail.
Teddy Horsley and Betsy Bear are blessed.

Everyone is happy.

Teddy Horsley is a bear who likes Sundays.

In *The Picnic,* Teddy Horsley and Betsy Bear's experience of preparing and celebrating a family picnic brings alive the nourishment and celebration at the heart of Holy Communion and the early disciples' experience of being fed by Jesus.

Not long afterwards another large crowd came together. When the people had nothing left to eat, Jesus called the disciples to him and said, 'I feel sorry for these people, because they have been with me for three days and now have nothing to eat. If I send them home without feeding them, they will faint as they go, because some of them have come a long way.' His disciples asked him, 'Where in this desert can anyone find enough food to feed all these people?' 'How much bread have you got?' Jesus asked. 'Seven loaves,' they answered. He ordered the crowd to sit down on the ground. Then he took the seven loaves, gave thanks to God, broke them, and gave them to his disciples to distribute them to the crowd; and the disciples did so. They also had a few small fish. Jesus gave thanks for these and told the disciples to distribute them too. Everybody ate and had enough – there were about four thousand people. Then the disciples took up seven baskets full of pieces left over.

Mark 8.1-9

The following questions suggest further ways of developing the links between the Bible passage and the young child's experience.

Talk about going on a picnic:
When do you like to go on a picnic?
Where do you go?
Who comes with you?
What do you like to take to eat?
What do you like to take to drink?
What do you like to do on your picnic?
What do you see? What do you hear? What do you smell?

Talk about the story:
Why does Teddy Horsley like Sundays?
What did Teddy Horsley and Betsy Bear take on their picnic?
What did they do on their picnic?
What did Mr and Mrs Henry do? And Lucy and Walter?
How did they all feel?
What did Teddy Horsley and Betsy Bear take to church?
What did they do in church?
What did Mr and Mrs Henry do? And Lucy and Walter?
How did they all feel?

Think some more about the story:
  What else might Teddy Horsley and Betsy Bear have taken on their picnic?
  What else might they have done?
  What else might they have taken to church?
  What else might they have done?

Think about the Bible passage:
  Imagine you are going with the crowd to see Jesus.
  Who do you go with? What do you see? What do you hear?

  Imagine what it feels like as the day gets later and you start to get hungry.
  What do you say? What do you hope?

  Picture Jesus feeding all the people with the bread and the fish.
  What is it like to be part of such a big picnic? What do you eat? What do you see? What do you hear? What will you tell your friends when you come home?

Titles in the series:

Good Morning	*Night-Time*	*Explorer*
The Grumpy Day	*Do and Tell*	*Neighbours*
The Present	*Music Makers*	*The Walk*
The Windy Day	*The Sunny Morning*	*Lights*
Autumn	*Water*	

Other publications to help young children explore the Bible:
Bible Storytime

Six books each containing twenty Bible stories from the Old and New Testaments, retold for the under sevens with related activities and prayer ideas.

Friezes

With clear, bold outlines for easy colouring and cutting out, NCEC friezes are ideal for use with children of all ages. As well as making traditional friezes, most of the material can be used to make 3-dimensional scenes. Based on a variety of themes:

Palm Sunday and Easter	*A Christmas Frieze*
The Christmas Story	*Harvest*
People of the World	*Feed the World*
Ministry of Jesus	*Stories Jesus Told*
The Early Church	*Make-it-yourself Bible Chart*